Aunt Flo

*who she is,
why she visits,
and what others have to say about her*

April Kurtyka

Dinocorn
Publishing

Dedicated to Ella, Apollo, and Guinevere
Thank you for inspiring me every single day

CONTENTS

CHAPTER 1:
Allow Me to Introduce You

People use many names to refer to Aunt Flo. You may know her as your period, big red, moon time, or even your little friend. If you haven't met her yet, I'm sure she will be visiting you soon. Some of you may eagerly await her arrival, while others dread her visits completely. I think it depends on how you learned about her, what it was like when you first met, and how the women around you treat her.

That's why I decided to write this book. I want to share what I've learned, but I also want to share experiences from other girls and women out there. In the grey shaded areas of this book you will hear about the great visit from Aunt Flo not just from me but also from girls all over the country—what their experiences were like, how they dealt with them, and what they wish they had been told.

Let's be honest; most of us don't enjoy talking about our bodily functions to just anyone. The problem is, we live in a culture that tends to view menstruation as an inconvenience or even an embarrassment. Some parents are so embarrassed about it that they refuse to even talk about it with their daughters. So where are you supposed to learn about what's going on with your body, both inside and out? Friends, media, school, Internet?

I remember how I was told about my body. I was about six years old, and my older sister used my pink-and-white flowered chalkboard, which I had only ever used when playing school with my dolls. She drew pictures of a woman's body and all of the changes that happen as puberty is reached. To say the least, her talk didn't inspire much confidence or excitement about what was to come for me. I certainly did not want to discuss what I had learned with anyone—I didn't know how much worse it was going to get!

My mother didn't know about the talk my sister had with me, and she never felt compelled to have one of her own, so I never really learned the truth until I was experiencing it for myself. I wasn't alone in not knowing; about 10 percent of girls will get their first period and not have any clue about what is happening or what they should do.

"I thought I had pooped my pants. It didn't click what was going on until the second pair of undies was dirtied." –C.K.

"I was ten when I received Mother Nature's special gift...although it didn't seem very special then...I was very embarrassed because I'm an only child and did not have any sisters to tell me what to expect; I was also the most developed for my age, so none of my friend had theirs either. I didn't really know what to do and honestly thought something was wrong with me. After about two days, I finally told my mom, and she was very understanding. She took me to the store to get what I needed. I was still very shy about it and did not tell my friends for probably about two years."–K.N.

"I had been told very little about what to expect. Body functions were viewed as gross, unnatural, and something to avoid at all costs. I came home from skiing and walked in the light rain, getting soaked to the bone and aching all over. I just wanted a warm bath and comfy PJs to snuggle in when I got home. When I did get home, I found blood on my underwear. Now I knew I'd hit a tree that day, but suddenly I thought I was dying from internal bleeding. Panic, fear overcame me as a shriek for my mom escaped me. My stepfather called to her and said, "She got it!" I was *so* embarrassed! My mom came in and told me how to put a pad on, and I jumped into a hot shower and wished it all away." –A.J.

For parents who are uncomfortable discussing the topic, some schools offer a "coming of age" talk. I must have been asleep the day they did that at my school because for the life of me, I cannot remember even one mention of periods in the classroom.

"I remember that day vividly in sixth grade, when all the boys went into the auditorium together and watched some movie about growing up and us girls could hear them laughing and hooting inside while we waited out in the hallway. Then we went in, after the boys shuffled out sheepishly and looked at us funny. I was very interested in the information, but most of the other girls were giggling and acting up and not taking it seriously." –S.C.

"When I was in fifth grade, we saw a movie about what happens when girls grow up. When I got home, my mom asked, "Do you have any more questions?" I didn't, but I will always remember that Mom said having periods was very special because it was a part of our special ability to have babies. Poor boys don't get that experience.
Three years later, when I was 13, I had my first period—finally, since several girlfriends were already having theirs. My friends and Mom were happy for me." –R.W.

But what happens if you aren't learning the basics at home or in school? Chances are you are getting your education from friends or the media. There is no shortage of magazine ads and commercials talking about the inconvenience, pain, and suffering that goes along with having your period. But take a step back and think about why the media makes periods look like such a hassle: it helps them sell their product. They have to convince you that periods are so horrible that you just cannot live without whatever it is that they are selling.

Here is the text from a popular pain reliever ad:
"Reverse the curse!
Cramps! Fatigue! Bloating! That's the reason it's called 'the curse.'"

But guess what? If you use their product, then all of your troubles will be solved. Hmmm, I don't think so! Don't get me wrong. I am not trying to imply that these items are not needed; some of them really are. But do we need to damage the way we look at our body just to sell a product?

"When I started my period, I knew what to do from my older sister and friends, but I never told anyone I got it. I kept it a secret for two years." – D.N.

"I remember that I started my period the summer after sixth grade. My sister and my mom had prepared me so I knew what it was, but we never really talked about it. It was all I could think about. I ended up going away on vacation for a week with a family who needed help with their kids. I remember being very secretive about it. My mom had bought me some teen magazines, and I remember going into a room by myself to read articles that other girls had written about the do's and don'ts of using pads, tampons, etc... It made me feel better to read those articles and not feel like I was all alone." –D.C.

Regardless of how you learned about your period and changing body, you need to know that your period is not a curse or anything to be ashamed of. Believe it or not, it's a sign that your body is working perfectly! Perhaps you really do feel uncomfortable or inconvenienced at times, but if we can figure out ways to make it less uncomfortable and less inconvenient, then perhaps we will start to respect our bodies more and even appreciate that we have these cycles every month.

Throughout the book, I will present you with a few thought-provoking questions and encourage you to journal your answers. You can write your thoughts here in this book or pick a special journal to write in.

Journaling is a great way to record your thoughts, experiences, and frustrations in a way that isn't scary. No one reads your journal unless you let them. Sometimes journaling is there for you when a friend or someone to talk to isn't. It's a safe place to let it all out. I encourage you to really think about your answers to the journaling questions I will present. There are no right or wrong answers—just write what you are feeling.

"Each time you make an entry into your journal, you open another door into yourself."
-Lucia Capacchione, M.A., *The Well-Being Journal*

JOURNAL

Where did you learn about your periods and the changes you are experiencing inside and out?

Who told you about it?

Do you wish you had found out another way?

How many negative commercials do you see about menstrual products during a TV show?

What questions do you have about your cycle?

CHAPTER 2:
Why Is Flo Here?

I have spoken with countless adults, both men and women, who cannot tell me exactly why we menstruate or what menstruation is exactly. Perhaps this lack of education is why some people call it a curse.

Maybe someone did try talk to you about menstruation but used clinical terms and explanations that were beyond your comprehension, so you just nodded your head in hopes that no one would realize you had no clue what they were saying. That's exactly what I did!

I want to lay it all out for you here in a way that will make sense to you. Don't worry; no one is watching, so if you don't get it the first time, you can just reread it until it all becomes crystal clear. But make sure you get it; we are talking about your body. Think of this as your owner's manual.

First things first; let's have a quick anatomy lesson. Your body is put together beautifully, and knowing how it all works can be extremely empowering. You have to know what you've got before you understand what it does and why.

Female Reproductive System

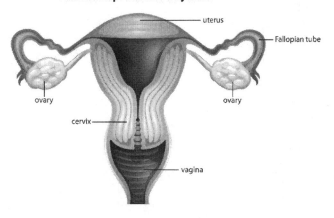

Take a second to look at the picture of the female reproductive system; you can refer to it now as we discuss the system's function.

Once a month, one egg will leave one of your ovaries. This is called ovulation—this is not menstruation. The egg goes into your fallopian tube (follow along with the picture, if you need to) toward your uterus. Your body gears up for this egg

12

release by releasing a hormone called estrogen. Estrogen stimulates your uterus to build up your endometrium, or lining of the uterus, with blood and tissue so that it's nice and thick and ready to cushion a baby if you make one. When your egg gets to the nice cushioned uterus, it waits to see if it will be fertilized by a sperm cell (from a man). If this happens, you will get pregnant. Obviously, when we are young, we aren't ready to be pregnant, but our bodies go through this process anyway; consider it practice.

If the egg is not fertilized when it gets to the uterus, it doesn't attach to the lining of the uterus. Your body knows that the egg isn't making a home there, so your uterus lets go of all of the extra blood and tissue. That is your period. It takes about 3–7 days for your uterus to let go of all of the blood and tissue, and then it builds a new lining all over again. Your period will come around every 24–34 days, and you will learn what your body's patterns are. The time between one period and the next is called your cycle. The first day of bleeding is day 1 of your cycle.

When you first begin having your periods, they may not come every month because your body is just getting used to this new function. It might take a year or more for your body to have a regular cycle. So try not to get frustrated when your sister or friend knows exactly when her period will come each month; you will eventually know that as well. It takes your body some time to establish its very own pattern.

 If you are having to change your pad, tampon, or cup every 1–2 hours, if you have bleeding lasting for more than seven days, or if you are suffering from extreme cramping or pain, let an adult know, just to make sure your body is functioning as it should.

"I felt pretty special and grown up. My mother was very open with me, so I didn't feel dirty or like something was wrong with me. I didn't see my period again for about two years because I was very physically active (in a ballet company). There's no doubt that it can be annoying and inconvenient, but the first time you get it really is one of the defining moments in a woman's life." –K.P.

"I remember my first two periods came fairly easily, and I had only a small amount of blood flow. I thought, "Oh, it's gonna be a piece of cake. What was all the fuss about?" Then, on my third period, things changed. My flow was heavier than I'd previously experienced. It wasn't so much that it was alarming. But I actually had to switch my pads out several times during the day." –C.T.

"The day I had my first period, I was nine years old and spending the night at my best friend's house. It was time to go to bed when I went to the bathroom and noticed some brown stuff on my underwear. I wasn't sure what it was, and I was too embarrassed to say anything to my friend or her parents, so I just changed my underwear and went to sleep. The next morning, I couldn't wait to get home and take a shower. I still wasn't exactly sure what was happening to me, but I had an idea it might be my

15

period. I knew periods were something that girls get, but none of my friends had gotten theirs and it wasn't something anyone had actually ever sat down and told me about. I was kinda freaking out in my head.

Once I got home and showered, I knew I would have to tell my stepmother that I thought I started my period, and I was agonizing over that. After I did get up the nerve to tell her, she was very surprised and then she kept hugging me! I was embarrassed enough that I certainly didn't want to make a bigger deal over it. And I definitely didn't want her to tell my dad and brother. I made her promise not to tell my brother, but I knew she was gonna tell my dad. I also made her promise me that Dad wouldn't tease me, and he actually didn't...until many years later when I was in my teens! After she explained to me what my period was and why we girls get it, she went to the store and got me some pads. I was too young for tampons (and I thought they looked way too scary), so I was glad she didn't get me those. At school the next day, I didn't tell any of my friends because I knew none of them had gone through this—and, again, I felt embarrassed. I kept it to myself. I thought there was nobody who would understand what was happening to me. As I walked around school with a pad on, I felt like everyone saw right through me and knew what had happened. I must have gone to the restroom a dozen times to make sure it wasn't leaking into my pants. Of course nobody ended up saying anything to me, and I was just glad for the day to be over! Once my period ended, I was so relieved that I could be normal again until I realized it was going to happen to me again the next month. I didn't get my period regularly that first year, which was OK with me, but it did get regular the next year and has been since. I was upset and embarrassed that this was happening to me, especially so young, but I just had to realize this is what happens to females as they grow up. I was on the long journey to becoming a woman, and that is nothing to be embarrassed about." –J.F.

"I can remember my first period very clearly. It was July 9, 1993, around nine o'clock at night. Two days after my thirteenth birthday. I was packing my

17

duffle bag for summer Bible camp in Colorado. I took a break to go to the bathroom, and that's when I noticed some reddish-brown marks in my panties. I knew exactly what it was, but I wanted to make sure. So I asked my mom to take a look. And she confirmed that my thoughts were correct. My initial reaction was excitement. It was like I had just joined the "women's club." At thirteen, I was still quite far from being a mature woman, but my period meant I was starting on that journey. I remember I didn't want my mom to tell my dad. I was a little embarrassed. Even though I knew my dad would understand, periods were a subject that I was taught you don't talk about with boys. My mom did tell my dad, though. I'm sure I was as red as a tomato. Dad just gave me a big hug and congratulations. I mumbled an embarrassed "thank-you" through my teeth and went to hide in my room. Then after the initial excitement, anxiety set in. I was leaving for camp early the next morning, and I was going to have my very first period! No mom. No other friends who had started. And no grown-up women to talk with if I had an issue. Plus, we would be driving on an old bus all the way to

Colorado! What if I had to use the bathroom? What if I had cramps? So many questions and concerns raced through my mind. I couldn't change my mind about going to camp. I talked my concerns out with my mom. She reassured me that I would be OK and that my period would most likely be very short because it was my first. She reassured me that no one would know just by looking at me that I had started. It was comforting, but I still was worried about the unknown period adventure that lay ahead of me.

So the morning came, and my period was still there, of course. My mom had so thoughtfully bought me the longest and thickest pads possible to use for my trip. Why my mom didn't choose to buy me thin pads with wings or even tampons, I'll never know. But it would have been much more comfortable than the thick diaper of a pad I had to wear on that eighteen-hour, ninety-degree bus ride we had to take all the way to Colorado! I look back now and laugh, but at the time, I don't think I could have been more uncomfortable. The flow of my period was not heavy at all. It was the cramps that really made me uncomfortable (and probably the heat in the bus!). My period lasted only three days, and I realized I had been worried over so many unnecessary concerns. It was really just the fear of the unknown, I believe. I look back on my first period, and I'm glad it happened the way it did."

–S.B.

If Flo hasn't made her first visit to you yet, don't worry; she will come! Your body doesn't know that all of your friends started their cycles already.

"I was fifteen and was very excited. Most of my friends got it much earlier than I did. I felt like a woman." –A.G.

"At first I was scared about bleeding, but my mom reassured me and made me feel safe about it. After our discussion, I was actually looking forward to starting my period. I remember that when I was about eleven or twelve, I started to get impatient, wondering when my body was going to hurry up and start bleeding." –K.W.

"In my family, it was seen as a major milestone in becoming a woman and moving into the next phase of growing up. I remember wanting to get it so badly because I felt that it meant I was no longer "just a kid." Plus, I was starting eighth grade at a new school, and I thought that all the 'cool girls' would have gotten their periods; I convinced myself that I had to get mine before school started." –L.B.

Do you think Flo is coming soon?
Your body has its own agenda that it will stick with. But you can look out for some clues that your body is going to start cycling soon so that you aren't totally caught off guard.

Have you noticed that your chest is a little tender lately? Or perhaps you already notice that your breasts are starting to grow. Breast development is a sign that your body is starting to change, becoming more feminine. Research shows that breast development will usually start around two years before a girl starts her menstrual cycle. So how long have you noticed that your breasts have been tender or are growing? That might give you a little hint as to how long you have until your period begins.

Another development you will notice before your period begins is hair growth in places you don't normally see hair. I'm sure some of you are nodding your head or rolling your eyes, thinking, "Yes! I was wondering why I all of a sudden had hair *there!*"

Hair growth in your armpits and around your vagina is a very normal sign of physical development. The hair there is usually very fine, and there is no need to do anything about it other than keeping it clean. If you are really bothered by it, then you need to talk with your parents regarding whether it would be appropriate to shave or trim the hair. Not every woman shaves, so do not feel like it's a mandatory part of becoming a woman. You need to do what you (and your parents) are comfortable with. A girl's first cycle can begin sometime around 4–6 months after she notices hair growth in her armpits and vaginal area.

There are also rumors that a girl needs to weigh around 100 pounds before her brain will be triggered to start her body's cycling. It does seem that the naturally tall and slender girls start a little later compared with their curvier peers. But I don't think there is concrete evidence to prove it.

Despite what you may have heard, there is no magic age when you start your period; it just depends on your body. Trust that it knows what it is doing and you will start your cycles when it's the right time for you.

Is it almost time for you to start?
Make a checkmark next to the sign that you have already experienced. The more checkmarks, the higher your chances of starting your period sooner rather than later:

○ Breast tenderness
○ Breast growth
○ Underarm hair
○ Pubic hair
○ Acne/breakouts
○ Weight at or above 100 pounds

Even if you aren't noticing any of the signs mentioned above, if you are around 10–16 years old, you should make sure you are always prepared by having a sanitary pad, clean pair of underwear, and plastic bag for your dirty underwear or clothes with you at school, at home, or when staying at a friend's house.

"I was the first girl in my class to start bleeding because I was so tall. I was barely twelve and weighed about 102 pounds (studies show that girls start bleeding when they weigh 98–100 pounds). I felt very special because I considered it evidence that I was growing up; plus, all of the girls in my circle of friends were chomping at the bit to start. I was honored by all those girls for being the first to begin, and they asked me many questions…I felt like my period was a reward of some sort for all of my travails." –E.M.

"I was at dance class when it started, and one of my friends had to track down a pad for me." –J. F.

"I had spent the night with my grandma and great aunt. I got up in the morning, and it had started. I wasn't scared or surprised, but, being with two older ladies, there were no "products" to use...of all times!" –J.A.W.

"My family had just returned from a summer road trip, and the power was out at our house. After being in the car for hours, I desperately needed to use the restroom. With a flashlight in hand, I ventured through the darkness to the bathroom only to discover that I had started my period. I shouted into the pitch black, hoping my sister would bring me a pad. Instead, my entire family showed up in the bathroom! Mortifying but memorable—and quite unexpected!" –D.J.

Now get ready for a story that sounds like it could be straight out of a movie. This is one woman's very unique (and totally true) story of how she became a woman on a ranch in Montana. I guarantee it will leave you thankful that you aren't rounding cattle and using rags for pads!

"We don't talk about our bodies in my family. By my family, I mean my parents and siblings and cousins on the ranch where I grew up. 'I broke my arm falling off a horse, but it doesn't hurt!' is probably as close as it gets to any real discussion.

We not only don't refer to it; we try to ignore it altogether. In my family, sleep is considered optional. Food only when necessary. You try to get by on as little as possible. And if you're sick, you don't take medication, don't get more rest, don't skip out on work. Nooooo. That's for city wimps and girly girls.

(And even if we are, technically, female, we'd never in our wildest dreams want to be girly girls. Nope. The girls in my family want to be men. But that's another story.)

So I was utterly amazed and humiliated that my mother, when I was about nine, turned in her seat to look at me over her shoulder and said, "You're going to start bleeding, um, uh, *down there*." First, I already knew that. Being a dutiful bookworm, I'd read all about menstruation and sex, and I knew possibly more than my parents did about the subject. I may have even had that special program in middle school where they take all the girls, giggling and squealing, into one auditorium and all the boys, looking solemn and a little afraid, into another and show us The Movie. I'm positive The Movie didn't talk much about how one got pregnant—more about the changes our bodies were going through.

Second, Mom had said—well, not said, but referred to—uh, you know. My vagina. How absolutely mort-i-fying! She'd broken the cardinal rule: We do not talk about our bodies. Limb hanging off? 'Uh, you might want to take a look at this?' A fever of 105 and pale as a ghost? 'I'm all right. Really. Let's go stack some bales.'

Third—and you won't believe this—my dad was right there. I mean, right there. Who talks about this stuff at all, much less with their dad *right there*? He of course didn't say anything, but still.

We had a VW van that we drove back and forth to town because it got good gas mileage. Dad drove, Mom rode on the passenger side, and—because these were the days before seatbelt use was enforced (or even considered)—I stood leaning against the huge hump between the front seats. I remember the exact spot on the road from town where she said it: on the blacktop highway before you turn onto the gravel road that eventually turns into a two-track, right near the little hill that had a natural flat spot where the boys from the juvenile delinquent home on our bus route spelled out dirty words with rocks.

When Mom said it, I felt my body clench with utter terror and embarrassment. What was she going to say next? She wasn't going to keep talking about it, was she? What if she got into the whole baby thing? I glanced at my dad. He was studiously, concentratedly, with minute interest, studying the road.

I should also say that none of the other four girls in my family had gotten The Talk. They had been gloriously left to their own devices, although they probably needed the talk more than I did, being fifteen to twenty-three years older than I was and living in a time when you couldn't find books on the subject in the library. As I stood leaning against the van's hump, I was green with envy for my sisters.

What was I going to do? She might go on! I clenched my hands in front of me and stared at the dirty gray carpet. I had to stop this! So I made a desperate attempt to head off what I was sure was coming. "I already know this, Mom," I whispered in a low voice, trying to sound confident, as though I had a firm grasp of the material and, if I were tested on it, would definitely get an A.

Mom glanced at Dad and then at me. She considered for a minute and then nodded her head and turned to face forward. That was it. I'd had The Talk. Whew. Normal family life could resume.

Meanwhile, at school, all the other girls were blossoming. In the locker room, they wore these beautiful lacy bras that covered their small but definitely growing breasts. The girls who actually had buds of breasts delicately sheathed in pink satin cups looked down on the girls whose flat chests sported 'training bras.'

The rate at which girls develop relates to their weight. Science suggests that girls have to reach a certain weight before the changes kick in. As a kid, I was always very slender. I remember in fourth grade I was taller than all the other girls and most of the boys, but I weighed only sixty-eight pounds. As a consequence, I was a late bloomer. I didn't have a bra or even a training bra; no curves whatsoever. I was slender and decidedly horsey.

Alisa, who was also from a ranch outside town and who had been my best friend until then, was the first to get breasts and the first to get her period. We all went to the rec center to go swimming, and she was the first to lounge wanly on the bleachers in the balcony because, whispered the swim teacher who was a short and well-muscled woman, 'it's that time of the month.'

The boys very quickly noticed these changes in Alisa, and she went from being a country bumpkin—and my friend—to being the most popular girl in school. I missed Alisa, but I understood the dynamics of popularity. If for some reason you were exalted, you had to just go with it. It was understood that a person shouldn't be held accountable for this bolt from heaven.

Each year during swim class, more and more of the girls took their turns up on those bleachers. I alternately eyed them jealously and, because of the way my family thought of the body, sniffed at their "frailty." But mostly I just felt ugly and gawky and unhappy with my body.

I turned twelve in January 1981. Still nothing. Heck, in another year and a half, I'd graduate from middle school to high school. Who ever heard of a high-schooler who didn't have her period? I could correct the boy who, after science class, said that girls have only one hole down there, but I couldn't say I'd had my period. Spring came and went, classes let out for the summer, and still nothing.

On the ranch, there are two main jobs: farming and ranching. Farming involves planting, irrigating, and harvesting alfalfa hay to be put up to feed the cows during the winter. Ranching involves herding the 1,200 head of cows and calves 60–100 miles on horseback or on foot from winter to summer pasture. It involves moving them from one pasture to another, depending on the dates of grazing leases, doctoring, branding, dehorning, castrating, tending horses, and fixing fence. In our case, it also involved the huge job of taking care of the people who came to experience ranch life as dudes.

My mom and dad did the farming, and my uncle's family did the ranching. It takes only a few people to irrigate and run the tractors for the farming side, so we kids all went up to the mountains during the summer to help with the ranching side.

We were at summer pasture at the Hank Lane place in the Pryor Mountains of Montana, which had been the 1920s homestead of a man from Germany. The tilting cabin and broken-down corrals rested at the base of steep mountains in a deep green valley, with its creek that tinkled over big white stones, disappearing underground for long stretches and then surfacing again.

That summer day when I was twelve, I was riding Ernie, a medium-sized sorrel horse with a short sorrel mane and tail. He was a good horse—not scary and unpredictable but not obstinate or hard-mouthed either. In other words, we were good friends.

I hadn't been feeling well. Of course, in my family, that did not mean that you got out of anything, but it must've been evident. It was the habit for anyone who wanted to—kids and dudes and sometimes cowboys—to lie down for a few minutes after lunch and then go back out to work. The previous day, my aunt had not woken me up after that nap to go to work in the afternoon, and I had slept until the sun had fallen behind the tall mountain. That was the only time in my whole life that this happened, and I woke up in a panic, sure I was in terrible trouble.

So, on this day, we rode up sagebrush-studded draws and then back down, shooing the cows we found into the main valley to be herded on to another pasture. Most of the dudes kept with the main herd, and I was sent on Ernie up a valley to gather cows.

My lower abdomen felt awful. It ached and pulled and twitched, and I felt a little like I had to pee, only it was different than that. I was confused. First, I couldn't separate the sensations, and second, I didn't have any experience to relate it to. Also, I didn't know if it was truly anything. Having spent most of my life ignoring my body, now that I tried to sense it and figure out what was going on, I didn't have the mental catalog to understand it.

I rode all the way up the draw and turned around and started gathering cows back down. I rose and fell in the saddle as Ernie trotted and loped. When we walked, I sat in the saddle and wondered if the resting of my pubic bone against the hard leather surface of the saddle could cause all this. Usually, the only time I got sore when I was riding was the first day or two after a long break from it, such as the first time in the spring. After that, I didn't get particularly sore—in my legs or crotch or anywhere.

Then I felt oozy liquid in my underwear. Oh my god! I had wet myself! How could this have happened? Even if I'd had to go pee—and I wasn't quite sure that was it—I hadn't had to go that bad. I hadn't wet my pants in my whole life that I could remember, other than a little leaking when I had to go really, really bad.

I glanced at the red-and-black backs of the cows in a line ahead of me. They could hear the cows out in the main valley, so they were increasing their pace to join the herd. Now was the time for me to find some bushes for a little privacy and find out what was going on. The cows would take care of themselves from here, but once we were in the main valley, I'd be with other people, which meant they would know I was looking for bushes to go to the bathroom.

At the edge of the draw where water periodically ran, the sagebrush had grown tall and provided a good screen. Ernie protested when I reined him off the worn game trail into the bushes. He shook his head, making the bridle tinkle, and tried to turn back. Like most horses, he hated to be alone and knew that the fastest way to get back to the other horses was to follow those cows. I insisted, reining him in harder, and he gave in and walked behind the bushes. I pulled back on the reins to stop him, and he stood chewing on his bit as I lifted my right tennis shoe from the stirrup and swung off his left side.

I debated whether to tie Ernie up so my hands would be free or to hold onto the reins. If I held onto the reins, it would be cumbersome to pull down my pants, but on the other hand, I was in a hurry. This also wasn't my first rodeo, as they say, and I had been left behind before by horses that should have been tied up. The horse spooks, especially when there are no other horses around, and jerks its head and snaps the leather rein, and off it goes, jogging home. Some horses have even mastered the art of gently pulling at the rein and working it free.

So I held Ernie's rein under my arm as I unsnapped and unzipped my jeans. As I was pulling them down my thighs, Ernie tugged a bit and almost toppled me over. I jerked the rein, and Ernie stopped and bobbed his head and stood. I pulled my pants past my knees and looked. There it was: dark red blood on my panties.

I knew immediately what it was. I had finally gotten my period! Finally. A surge of excitement went through me. It was true. I had finally gotten what all the other girls had. I wasn't as much of a freak or a weirdo as I'd thought. I had reached that milestone.

Everything else clicked into place. It explained why I had been feeling bad. So this is what it feels like, I thought. These are what cramps are. (Little did I know that my cramps were really hardly anything. Most of the time, my experience of them is very mild compared to other women's experiences.)

Now I would be up on those rec center bleachers too. Now it was possible for me to get pregnant.

But then it hit me like a ton of bricks. This would happen once a month for the rest of my life. The rest of my life. Every month for as long as I lived, I would get a period. (I was only vaguely aware of menopause.) Guys didn't have to deal with this. Then it felt like a curse. I felt the weight of it and the future on me.

I tried to clean up, but we never carried water or tissue or anything with us. Sagebrush boughs are very prickly and unsuited to the task, so I found a stick that had been smoothed by water, and then I scraped away as best I could. It didn't do much. I pulled up my sticky panties and my pants and hoped it wouldn't soak through. Then I got back on Ernie and rode after the cows.

For the rest of the day, I thought about it. As I pushed my little herd of cows into the larger one in the main valley, I thought how long a lifetime is. When I waved at the dudes, I wondered if I appeared different. When we came to another huge valley and I trotted in among trees and hawthorn bushes, I tried to figure out what I would do about the bleeding. We were a hundred miles from any town, so I couldn't go to a store. I couldn't ask my mom, and my sisters were all off to college or married. I felt shy about talking to my aunt.

That night after supper and all the chores, I went down to the creek and washed myself below where we drew water. I scrubbed the panties as best I could with a bar of soap. I made some rags out of an old shirt and lined a clean pair of underwear with them. The rags quickly soaked through overnight, so I had to approach my aunt.

I don't remember my aunt's reaction when I told her. It was very businesslike, I'm sure; that is her nature, and she has daughters. She promised that on her trip to town in a day or two, she would pick up some pads—she didn't have any as she was past menopause. I got the impression from something she said that, in her opinion, good girls wear pads and wouldn't dream of wearing tampons. I limped by with rags until, in a few days, she pulled me aside and handed me a bulky box of pads still in the grocery sack.

My first impression of a pad was that it felt like I had a diaper on. They were so huge and bulky. And then there were the problems of disposing of them where the dogs didn't get at them and carrying them with you on a horse. Luckily that period was almost over.

It wasn't until at least a couple of months later that, under the guidance of one of my older sisters, I started using tampons. They were so much more convenient—and you didn't have to skip swimming and be embarrassed, I found out, by everyone knowing you had your period. However, the first time I used them, I did it wrong. I didn't read the directions and didn't put them in nearly far enough, and they rubbed and hurt and were really uncomfortable. This can't be how it is, I thought, and read the directions. Another of my sisters pursed her lips about using tampons. She'd used one, but then she'd forgotten to take it out after a period and had to go to the doctor to have it removed.

This first period was a momentous occasion for me, as it is for all girls, but possibly in a different way. In my family, it was not celebrated. Rather, it was a shameful thing, something you didn't talk about, something you hid. Your body in general was a shameful thing. Also, you were valued for how much you were like a man—working hard out of doors, being tough, being independent. Getting my period was a relief because I could be like the other girls, but it was also a sign of weakness because it reminded me of my body and that I was a girl, not a boy." –T. L.

JOURNAL

If you could make your cycle start at the "perfect time," when would that be? What would your day 1 story be?

What worries you most about starting your period?

Who would you/can you tell, or who will help you when you start?

CHAPTER 3:

How to Make Flo Feel Welcome

"I was relieved that I did not have to wonder every day anymore if it was going to happen at a terrible time and was happy that I was normal." –L.L.

Your period may bring with it some aches and pains that you probably have heard women (and men) refer to as PMS. PMS stands for premenstrual syndrome, and many women report that they experience it every month. This change in your hormones begins about a week before your period starts and can cause you to feel a little sensitive, depressed, irritable, bloated, and/or achy overall. Not everyone experiences these symptoms every month, so don't worry about it. The more you listen to your body, by resting and staying hydrated and well-nourished, the less extreme your symptoms should be.

"About two weeks prior to my cycle, my breasts are tender and painful to touch. I crave sweets, and I always seem hungry. I eat constantly." –A.T.

"Some months I seem to get a hormonal headache the week before my period starts. Other months my breasts are overly sensitive and are painful to the touch or when I am active. It reminds me that my body is going to need to slow down and rest for a few days." –J. F.

Every girl is different, but when you get your first period you can expect that first bit of blood to be only a small amount and more pinkish at first. The amount of blood will increase in your next few cycles, and the color will usually become a bit redder. You may experience a little cramping very low in your abdomen, and you may have a low backache and sometimes a headache; these are all normal symptoms. Your body is really asking for a little time out right now. If you can decrease your activity, even just a little bit, your body will appreciate it, and you will generally have less severe symptoms. And that is what we are all

44

shooting for!

"My period symptoms are not intense. I get a mild cramping every once in a while in my lower back or abdomen. Sometimes I will experience sensitivity in my breasts for a few days as well." –S.K.

When you can look at your period as a positive occurrence, a sign that your body is working beautifully on its own, you can tap into your body's wisdom and give it what it wants during that time. Maybe you need a little rest or a warm bath, or possibly some time to reflect and journal about how you are feeling. There will be many more ideas about how to manage your discomforts in chapter 5.

The following are some ways you can celebrate your first cycle and honor all of the cycles that follow. Don't be afraid to make your period a time you actually look forward to instead of a time you dread.

Take out a highlighter or pen and mark the ideas that you want to try. You can pick more than one to do, or perhaps you can pick a new one each month.

• Have a "red" party: invite only those who have started their cycle, and have them all dress in red. At the party, people can share their experiences (try to keep them positive) and give you tips they have picked up along the way.

"We made a cake and had a welcome-to-womanhood celebration" –S.R.

• Create a necklace or bracelet that you wear only during menstruation. You can use stones like citrine, moonstone, or malachite that are known to help alleviate discomforts, or you can use beads that have blessings from friends and family members (perhaps given to you at your red party).

• Go out for a meal with just your mother.

"To celebrate my first cycle, my mom took me shopping and to lunch. I bought my first pair of Birkenstocks! I remember it like it was yesterday."
–C.E.

"The morning my daughter got her first signs, she called me into the restroom and showed me. She had cleaned herself and had gotten a cloth pad (that had already been in her special drawer), and as I got her new panties, she took a shower. Once she was ready, we went to the store and got her some special gifts and went to the restaurant of her choice. She brought her younger sister along, and it was a Ladies Day. There was no fear, no panic, no sorrow. It was joyful, fun, and a bonding time. It honestly brought her and me closer than we have ever been!"
–A.J.

• Go out for a meal with just your father.

"My dad took me to the only restaurant in town, Chinese, just him and me for dinner, because I was a grown woman now." –S.H.

47

"I prepared my daughters in advance and then gave them a red rose to signify to them the beginning of their journey to being a woman. Then my husband and I had a special dinner for them, and we all toasted to their journey, using their favorite fruit juice and soda." –I.S.

• Start a journal that you write in only during menstruation. You can collect any thoughts and feelings you might have about what you are experiencing or anything else that is happening in your life. Make a list of the things that were nourishing and made you happy in the past month.

• Paint your nails red.

• Menstruation is a time when your body is asking for a little rest. You can support this by giving yourself permission to rest and relax. Take some time to do whatever helps you relax deeply: yoga, meditation, deep breathing, walking in nature, etc.

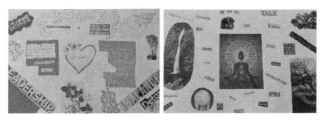

● Make a collage or "vision board" by using drawings, poems, and inspiring words/pictures from magazines.

● If you are feeling angry, grouchy, or just plain irritable, write down everything that's bothering you. You can do this in your journal or anywhere you choose at that moment.

● Take a bath with lavender or rose petals.

● Stay warm. Keep your hands and feet warm.

● Write down all of your dreams, no matter how silly they seem.

- Curl up in a blanket.

- Turn off the TV, the bright lights, and your computer. Try to use soft lighting or even candlelight.

- Take a "special day."

"I had talked to my daughter about starting her period and what it meant to begin menstruation, etc... I told her that although we didn't know exactly when it would start, wherever she was, she would have a 'free' day to celebrate the fact that she was experiencing this special rite of passage into becoming a woman. I explained it may happen in the middle of the night, or while she was with friends or at school or anywhere...and if she was not with me when it occurred, she should call me and could then do *absolutely anything* she wanted to do—a special celebration. Every now and again we would talk about the impending event, and she was excited to celebrate it whenever it came...and then one morning we were up early. I was getting ready for work, she was getting ready for school. When I came out into the kitchen, I noticed she was sitting on the couch. I asked her why she wasn't continuing to get ready, and she said, 'Today is the "free" day!' I was so excited I jumped up and down and had a laundry list of ideas of what we could do to celebrate her budding womanhood." –J.T.

JOURNAL

Which of the celebration ideas were your favorites?

Do you have any other ideas that weren't on the list?

CHAPTER 4:

How to Manage Flo

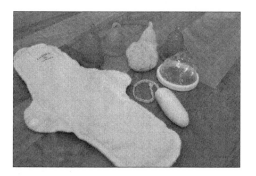

Alternative Menstrual Products

I'm sure you've heard about tampons and pads, but did you know that there are different types of each? And did you know that there are more options for you than just tampons and pads during your periods?

I really encourage you to experiment with a few different types of menstrual products. Just because you don't know anyone who has used it doesn't mean it's not the perfect item for you. You just have to give it a try. The great thing is, if you don't like it, you never have to use it again!

Sanitary Pads

Both cloth and disposable pads come in a variety of sizes , designs and absorbencies

With sanitary pads, you have many options, believe it or not! First, you have cloth or disposable. Then you have to consider length and thickness (or absorbency). At first it may be hard to decide what kind of absorbency you need until you've had a few cycles and know what your flow is like. I am a worrywart, so I started out with the super absorbent and then went down as needed. You can do what feels right for you.

The first time you use a pad, experiment a little. Find the underwear that are the most comfortable while using a pad; full back underwear are usually best. Even though it will feel like you are wearing a diaper and you will feel like everyone can tell you're wearing it, chances are no one has any idea. However, in the beginning, you may want to wear looser clothing until you feel a little more comfortable wearing pads. Also, once you find the right thickness and absorbency, you won't have to wear a pad that feels like a diaper; you can find the one that fits the contours of your body the best.

"My mom…gave me these *huge* pads and my very first pair of granny panties 'cause the pad was so big it would not fit in my regular underwear" –J.F.

I suggest that you change your pad every few hours, but this will really depend on your flow. In the beginning, just make a quick stop in the bathroom every few hours to see how full your pad is.

If you decide to try cloth pads (or reusable pads), the rules are the same. You will want to check in

 every so often to see how full it is getting. When you are ready to change your pad, make sure you have a wet bag (see picture), and you can put it right in there. As long as you take proper care of your pads and your wet bag, there shouldn't ever be any noticeable smells.

There are many different methods to cleaning cloth pads, and instructions should come with your pads when you buy them. But generally you will soak them for a while in cold water and then either put them in the washing machine or wash them by hand. Pretty darn easy!

"Since making the switch to cloth pads and organic tampons, a lot of the uncomfortable side effect/symptoms of my periods (itching, dryness) that I had always assumed were normal went away. I have to assume that I had been reacting to the bleaches, chemicals, scents, etc. in disposable products. I haven't had any of those issues since switching to cloth." –J.F.

Tampons

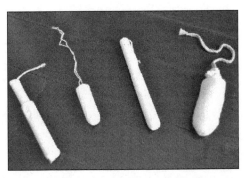

Different tampons: Natracare with applicator, OB (no applicator),
Tampax with applicator, and cloth.

Tampons are often a little intimidating at first.
Sticking something "up there"? Won't it get lost?
The answer is no, it can't get lost in there. However,
some girls do forget that they have a tampon
inserted, which can create infection and put them at
risk for toxic shock syndrome. Toxic shock
syndrome is a rare, life-threatening complication
involving a bacterial infection. It has been
associated with the use of superabsorbent tampons,
so make sure you are using the appropriate
absorbency, and always remove your tampon a few
hours after inserting it.

If you have a phone, there are apps you can

download that will help you remember when you put your tampon in and when to change it. Tampon Timer and Tampon Minder are two popular apps you can try. These will obviously work just as well for helping you remember your pads, cups, or sponges too.

"I never knew how to use a tampon until I was twenty—my mom never brought it up, and I just kept using pads and wore two pairs of underwear during my cycle. I look back and cringe at how unaware I was." –J.F.

As with sanitary pads, you have the option of cloth or disposable tampons; however, cloth is a little harder to find. The disposable tampons come in many different sizes and also give you the option of applicator versus no applicator. An applicator is a cardboard or plastic tube that makes tampon insertion easier for some girls.

With tampons, it's very important to know your anatomy. You don't want to just shove the tampon into your vagina; you want to know exactly where you are putting it, at what angle, and where it is supposed to sit. Before trying to insert a tampon, it might be a good idea to use a handheld mirror and take a look at your own anatomy so that you have more confidence about trying it. I suggest using the smallest-sized tampon possible; you can always use a bigger one if necessary for a heavy flow after you get used to inserting them.

All tampons should come with instructions; however, here is a quick rundown of how to insert a tampon that comes with an applicator:

> —First, make sure to wash your hands with soap and water. With dry hands, unwrap the tampon. It's OK to be a little nervous! However, if your nervousness makes you drop your tampon, make sure to just throw it out and get a new one.

> —Sit or stand in a comfortable position. Some girls prefer to place one leg on the toilet seat or tub, others prefer to squat down, and others just sit on the toilet. After

you find a comfortable position, hold the tampon with the fingers that you write with. Hold the middle of the tampon at the spot where the smaller, inner tube inserts into the larger, outer tube. The round part of the tampon or applicator should be facing you. Make sure the string is visible and pointing away from your body.

—Hold the tampon at the opening of your vagina. Gently push the tampon into the opening, aiming for the small of your back. Stop when your fingers touch your body and the applicator, or outer tube, is completely inside the vagina.

—Once the applicator, or outer tube, is inside your vagina, use your index finger to push the inner tube (the tube where the removal string is visible) through the outer tube. This pushes the tampon into the vagina.

—Once the inner tube is all the way in, use your thumb and middle finger to remove the applicator, or outer tube. Be sure the string hangs outside of your vaginal opening. Later, when you are ready to remove the tampon, hold the string and gently pull it downward until the entire tampon is out.

You might want to try doing a few "test walks" in the comfort of your own home. If you feel the tampon or it just feels uncomfortable, readjust. Usually, that means it's not in all the way and just needs to go in a bit further. Remember, it won't get lost in there!

"My mother handed me a tampon and said to just put it in. I was not sure how and came out with it hanging halfway out. It sure did make sitting uncomfortable!" –C.S.

If you try a tampon without an applicator, you will follow the same steps as above; however, instead of pushing in the

applicator, you will use your pointer finger to push the tampon into your vagina until it feels comfortable.

A cloth tampon functions pretty much the same as a  disposable; however, you don't throw it in the trash can when it's full. You will place it in a wet bag just like you did with the cloth pads. Then soak, wash, and reuse!

Still having tampon troubles?

—Use a little olive or coconut oil. Smear it all over the tampon and insert it again. The extra lubrication should make it a little easier. Remember that this is only for learning how to insert it. The oil will keep the tampon from absorbing any blood, so it's important to remember that this is just for practicing.

—Relax. Take a deep breath and make sure your jaw is not clenched. Some believe that if your mouth is tense, your vagina will be too. This is normally a rule to remember for childbirth, but I think it applies to tampon insertion as well.

—Try to use a tampon when you aren't on your period. This will make the process a little less messy, and there will be less pressure on you to make it work right at that moment. The only drawback here is that you won't have the natural lubrication that blood provides, so make sure to use oil, like I mentioned above.

—If it's not working right now, don't force it! Just try again at another time. Trying over and over again will cause not only more frustration but also vaginal pain and soreness.

Whether you are using pads or tampons, I encourage you to buy the organic cotton and bleach-free kind. When tampons are made out of rayon (like most are) they have been bleached. The problem with this is that it can dry out the natural lubricant your body makes and needs. Another by-product of the bleaching is dioxin. Dioxin is a known carcinogen (cancer-causing agent) that can collect in your fatty tissues and potentially put you at risk for cancer or endometriosis (a disease of the lining of the uterus). Although you may use regular pads and tampons your entire life with no issues, I encourage you to reduce your risk of cancer and disease by buying only bleach-free products.

Sea Sponges

I bet you are wondering if I am totally crazy right now. Sea sponges? In your vagina? Yes! Sea sponges can be used just like tampons. They are comfortable, soft, and textured similarly to the vaginal wall. Most sea sponges can be trimmed to fit your vagina perfectly, so they don't cause any discomfort. They are cost effective and convenient because you don't have to carry any with you when you go out; just rinse out the one you have and put it back in.

However, don't go down to the beach and pick up some sponges. Make sure that you buy your sponges from a reputable company; I like Sea Pearls from Jade & Pearl.

Here are Jade & Pearls' instructions for insertion:
"Wash hands thoroughly before handling your
sponge. Wet your sponge with warm water, and
then squeeze out excess water. Squash your sponge
and gently push into your vagina until it feels secure
and comfortable. If you have trouble inserting your
sponge this way, you can try using a reusable
applicator.

If you feel any pressure, remove your sponge and
trim it to a smaller size. Do not cut the sponge in
half, as Sea Pearls are trimmed to a specific shape.
Rather, hold the sponge and trim around the
perimeter about 1/8 inch at a time until you reach
the desired size. If your sponge is the proper fit, you
should not feel it."

"I don't like the cup because it's not a natural
material. I use only sea sponge. It's fabulous; I've
been using it for twenty years. A set of two lasts
almost six months. You just need to be mindful
about squeezing it out into your plants or the sink
and rinsing every few hours on that one heavy
bleeding day. Rinse with lemon juice or apple cider

vinegar if it seems a bit smelly. Then when your period is over, boil and stash it in a cotton baggie in your purse until next month. Once you are used to it, you will never believe people consider using tampons. Took me about six hours to get used to it."
–J.L.

Menstrual Cups

We are so fortunate that we have so many choices for menstrual products! My grandmother recently told me that she had to wear rags made from old sheets during her cycle! I'm glad that we have evolved from there.

Menstrual cups look a bit intimidating to anyone, no matter what your age. The good news is that they aren't so hard to use; you just have to practice a bit. I wouldn't try a cup on a day you are going to school or work. I would wait for a weekend when you can experiment a little and not worry if there is a little bit of leaking.

"I use the Diva cup and like it; my biggest thing is that my flow can be heavy, so I definitely can tell when it is time to empty it because it starts to slip out of place. I also find that I do still have to use a small pad for slight leakage. I think maybe sometimes I don't get it in right because it feels uncomfortable while I'm running and exercising. I love that it cost less than three months of pad purchases; it has more than paid for itself. It is not uncomfortable at all except when it's time to empty it, and it's also very easy to insert." –J.B.

"When Aunt Flo is around, I use the MeLuna cup. I love it! Soooo much easier and more comfortable than tampons. I tried it, and it was awesome. Never going back!" –M.N.

Before you insert a menstrual cup you need to wash your hands with soap and water. You should wash the cup off with warm water as well. You will then need to fold the cup to make it easier to insert. There are a few different folds that you can try, here is one of the easiest:

 The "U-Fold": You press the sides
of the cup together (by the opening)
and then fold it in half again.

—Once you pick the type of fold that you
want to use, hold the folded sides firmly in
place between your thumb and forefinger so
that the curved edge is facing away from
your palm (or so that the stem is facing your
palm).

—Insert: While you are in a comfortable
position and with your vaginal muscles
relaxed, gently separate the labia with your
free hand and then push the curved edge of
the folded cup horizontally into the vaginal
opening so that the tip of the stem is no
further than 1/2 inch into the vagina.
Inserting your cup up too high in the vagina
could potentially cause leaks and may also
make removing it a bit harder.

—Finally, you will want to make sure that
it's sealed (that it won't spill): To do this,

you will want to grip the base of the cup (not the stem) and turn the cup one full rotation (360 degrees) in either direction. Your cup should rotate easily to ensure that it is fully open (no longer folded) and positioned horizontally toward your tailbone.

—To remove, pull gently on the stem of your cup until you can reach the base of the cup. Pinch the base of the cup to release the seal and continue to pull down to remove it. After the cup has been removed, empty the contents in the toilet. Wash your cup well with warm water and reinsert.

Your cup should be emptied, washed, and reinserted at least twice in a 24-hour period and can be worn overnight without concern of leaking. By monitoring the fullness of the cup over a couple of cycles, you will quickly learn how often to empty it according to your specific needs. Most girls find that the cup is not even half full after twelve hours. For those with heavier flows, the cup is simply emptied more often.

To really clean the cup, some choose to wash it with soap daily. If you do this, make sure to use a cleanser sold by a menstrual cup company or a fragrance free soap. You can also sterilize it once a month by submerging it in boiling water for about five minutes. Check the instructions that come with the cup since many suggest different boiling times.

"I've been using a cup for about two years, and I swear by it! Whenever I get the chance to explain it to people, I get extremely excited because if I hadn't been digging through the Internet one day. I would never have known what a cup was. It does take some practice and refinement to use it properly, but with all the benefits, it's definitely worth learning. It's also a lot safer and more eco-friendly than anything else." –S.A.

"I've been using the Lunette cup for over two years. I really had to figure out the most comfortable way for me, and I ultimately cut off the stem and inverted it to make it wearable. I bought a MeLuna about a year later, and that changed my life. Before using cups, my period was a full nine days and very heavy. Now it's about four days with one heavy day. I forget about it some days! The best part? No strings to worry about in the summer! Because I'm not using tampons that remove all the moisture from my vagina, I have lighter, less worrisome periods. I tell everyone about cups! Really! I read about them ten years ago. At first I was too nervous about the 'gross factor' to try them, but I got over it. Better late than never." –K.R.

JOURNAL

Cloth, disposable, tampons, cups, sponges... Which one do you want to try? (Or do you want to try them all?)

Do you know anyone who uses an alternative menstrual product? If so, could you talk to them about it?

Are you active in sports? Does this affect your decision on what type of menstrual product to use?

CHAPTER 5:

How to Stay Comfortable When Flo Visits

There is no rule that states being on your period means you have to be miserable. That's entirely up to you. Sure, sometimes you will want to rest more, eat more, or ask for a little more nurturing, but that's OK! That means you are listening to your body and what it's asking for at that moment.

I'm thankful for being a woman and having my menstrual cycles. Stick with me here; don't roll your eyes just yet. Our bodies tell us every month that we need to get more rest and pay attention to our body and its needs. This is a gift! I know that in our incredibly busy world, no one has time to be inconvenienced with rest, but really, our bodies and minds need it. I am not suggesting that you lie in bed and do nothing your entire period, but I am suggesting you honor your body by taking a little more rest time when you need it. Men would benefit from a monthly reminder to rest as well!

That said, sometimes we do get crampy and need a little relief. I suggest trying out some natural ways to help your body first; you might be surprised at how powerful they can be.

"I don't mind having a period; what I don't like are the symptoms." –J.L.

—**Baths:** A nice warm bath can be soothing for your mind and body. Maybe light a few candles so you don't have the lights screaming at you, add some bubbles or essential oils—and you've got it made. Who wouldn't want to do this—cramps or no cramps?

—**Iron:** Don't forget that when you are losing blood, you are also losing iron. Generally it's totally fine and your body is ready for it; however, eating more iron-rich foods during this time could certainly help with your energy levels. Examples of iron rich foods are spinach, sweet potatoes, peas, broccoli, string beans, beef, lamb, ham, turkey, chicken, tofu, strawberries, watermelon, raisins, dates, figs, and prunes.

If you are experiencing overwhelming fatigue during this time and eating iron-rich foods isn't helping, I suggest that you see your midwife, doctor, or gynecologist. They might want to do some bloodwork to check on your iron levels.

—**Warm compress:** This is super easy and can really help! You can just find a towel that will be large enough to cover your pelvic area from hip to hip. Submerge the towel in hot/warm water (you can also add some essential oils to the water as well). Squeeze out excess water so it's not dripping and apply it to your pelvic area. You can now cover with a dry towel to help keep some of the warmth in.

Hot water bottles are also great because they conform to the shape of your body nicely and hold the heat for a much longer period of time.

Rice socks are similar to hot water bottles; they, too, conform to the body nicely and keep their heat for a while. You can easily make your own rice sock by getting a large sock and filling it with uncooked rice. Just knot or sew the top to finish it; don't use staples or a rubber band because you will be putting it into the microwave. Then put it in the microwave for 1–2 minutes—and voilà! You have your own awesome heat pack.

"During my heavy flow days, I tend to have more pressure and aching in my pelvic floor area. I love my rice sock on these days; it helps that area and my entire body to relax."
–J.F.

You also have the option of using portable heating pads that you can just buy at the store and stick onto your pelvis. Hopefully you've seen the underlying theme here: heat will help dissipate cramps.

"I just use a heating pad and try to relax as much as possible and not do anything strenuous" –K.W.

—**Essential oils:** As an aromatherapist, of course I love essential oils. Most people just think they smell good—but that is just the beginning. Essential oils can be used help relieve many of the discomforts you may experience before and during your period. When using essential oils, it's very important to use only high-quality oils with no fillers. Also, always make sure to test them on a small patch of skin before using them to make sure there is no reaction.

Here is an incredibly powerful blend from Valerie Gennari Cooksley's book, *Aromatherapy: Soothing Remedies to Restore, Rejuvenate, and Heal.*

A Potent Premenstrual Potion
(a massage oil for PMS symptoms)

2 tbsp. vegetable oil

2 tbsp. arnica or St. John's Wort oil

2 tsp. evening primrose or borage oil

20 drops lavender essential oil

10 drops rosemary essential oil

6 drops clary sage essential oil

6 drops juniper essential oil

6 drops lemon essential oil

Add the essential oils to an amber glass bottle. Then add the infusion and vegetable oils. Shake gently to mix well. Label contents with directions for use. To apply, massage a small amount of the oil to the lower abdominal region and low back area. Apply the aromatic oil with gentle hand pressure, working toward the heart to encourage blood return and to increase lymphatic drainage. Inhale essences from the hands after application. Apply daily during episodes of PMS symptoms, up to two weeks prior to menses.

If you just want one or two oils to help during this time, you can try some of the following: clary sage, sweet fennel, geranium, and rose will all influence the production of hormones. Bergamot, Roman chamomile, and rose may reduce feelings of depression and irritability.

"At the first sign of cramps, I rub a little clary sage and lavender on my belly; it provides quick relief for me." –A.K.

—Time alone: Have you ever noticed that there are certain times of the month when you just want to scream at every person who even looks at you? Perhaps it's best to distance yourself from people as much as you can. Of course you will have to see people at school and any activities you participate in, but other than that, keep a low profile until you feel like you can handle being around people again.

I suggest even letting your parents know that you are feeling this way; ask that they allow you more time to yourself. Maybe give it a nickname or something that's easy to reference. Tell them you are need some alone time or that its your "rest week"; just pick something easy to remember and understand. That way, you won't have to get angry when you feel like they aren't giving you the space you need. If they know it's that time again, they will be better able to help you by giving you that time.

Long ago women went into a separate area or tent during their period. The red tent, as it was called, was the place where women gathered during their cycles of birthing, menstruation, and even illness. This was a time of rest, reflection, and sisterhood for women. They looked forward to this period of time to rest their body. You may be wondering how this was possible if women had their period at different times of the month. Well, back then, before birth control and distance from other women affected periods, women often menstruated at the same time. It's something that many women still experience when they live closely with another woman; it's referred to as menstrual synchronicity.

So this idea of resting and taking time away from "normal life" during your period has been there from the beginning of time; let's not put an end to something our body is so clearly asking for.

—**Journaling:** This is a great activity to do during your alone time. I used to really hate journaling; then I realized it wasn't journaling I hated but rather the worry that someone might find what I had written down. I didn't want people to know my deepest thoughts. Well, there are a couple ways around that.

Option 1: use a journal that is locked up, or find a way to store it where it can be locked.

Option 2: safely burn or shred your writings when you are done with them.

Please do not burn things in your room or in a place that's not meant for burning. Getting rid of the journal entries gives you a sense of freedom. You got it out of your mind and off your chest, and now you never have to worry about another person seeing your most intimate thoughts.

—**Water:** Did you know that many girls experience weakness and fatigue during Flo's visit because they are simply dehydrated? When you are losing more blood and fluid than normal, it is extra important to drink plenty of water every day. The easiest way to do this is to always carry a water bottle with you so you can drink when thirsty. If you drink to thirst, your body should stay hydrated and maintain energy. If you are looking for specific numbers in regard to how much you should drink, take your body weight and then divide it in half—that's how many ounces you should drink. So, if you weigh 100 pounds, you should drink about 50 ounces of water per day. However, I really encourage you to listen to your body. Drink water when you are thirsty, and you can't go wrong.

—**Tea:** If you enjoy the taste of tea, there is a tea that can really help with your PMS symptoms. It's called red raspberry tea, and it's very easy to find in most grocery stores. You can take comfort in the fact that there are currently no known side effects to enjoying this tea and natural menstruation discomfort remedy. Raspberry leaf tea is full of nutrients including iron; calcium; manganese and magnesium; and vitamins B1, B3, C, and E. It's known to tone your uterus, which helps to alleviate your cramps and regulate your bleeding.

Many other herbs and teas might help you during your cycle. I just wanted to highlight one that is very popular and easy to find here.

"I'm a big fan of teas meant for 'womanly' health—especially red raspberry leaf."
–L.B.

—**Yoga:** You can try many different types of yoga; however, when you are on your period or right before, I suggest you try some very relaxing, nonstrenuous yoga poses. Yin and Restorative yoga are two types of classes that you might really enjoy during this time. If it's tough to make it to a class—or maybe you just don't feel like leaving your house—here are some poses that you can do to provide comfort in the comfort of your own home.

Wide Child's Pose:

If you feel cramps in your lower back, this pose is sure to offer relief.

—Place your knees on the floor, widen them to a comfortable distance, and then fold forward, extending your arms in front of you.

—Rest your forehead on the mat or turn your head to one side. Stay here as long as you want.

Legs-up wall pose (Viparita Karani):

"Lying on the floor and placing one's feet against the wall, as high up as possible, will alleviate cramps in a matter of fifteen minutes. My dance teacher in college used this tactic anytime we came in complaining, and we were up doing triple pirouettes within thirty minutes every time." –J.S.

—Find an open wall space. Start seated beside the wall, with your feet on the floor in front of you and the left side of your body in contact with the wall. On an exhale, gently lie down on your back and pivot yourself so that the backs of your legs are pressing against the wall and the bottoms of your feet are facing up. You may need to

wiggle around to find your way into this
position.

—Your sitting bones should now be pressed
up against the wall or slightly away from it,
and your back and head should be resting on
the floor.

—If you find this position uncomfortable in
any way or just wish for extra cushion, you
can use a blanket here. Pressing the bottoms
of your feet into the wall, lift your hips
slightly and slide your prop underneath your
hips.

—Stay here for 5–15 minutes. To come out
of the position, push the bottoms of your
feet into the wall and lift your hips slightly.
Gently roll to one side, being sure to slide
your support out of the way if you have used
one. Stay on your side for a few breaths
before getting up.

Bridge Pose (Setu Bandha Sarvangasana):

—Lie on your back on the floor, and if you would like to do so, place a thickly folded blanket under your shoulders to protect your neck. Bend your knees and set your feet on the floor, heels as close to the sitting bones as possible.

—Exhale and, pressing the inner part of your feet and arms actively into the floor, lift your bottom off the floor. Keep your thighs and feet parallel.

—Lift your bottom until the thighs are about parallel to the floor. Keep your knees directly over the heels, but push them forward, away from the hips, and lengthen the tailbone toward the backs of the knees.

—Lift your chin slightly away from your chest and, firming the shoulder blades against your back, press the top of your chest toward your chin.

—Stay in the pose for thirty seconds to one minute. Release with an exhalation, rolling the spine slowly down onto the floor.

—**Understand your rhythm:** This might sound a little strange, but every month you go through emotional cycles. If you learn what your cycles are, you can learn to expect when to feel high or low and be ready for that by making sure not to schedule things when your introverted mood is coming up. How can you learn what your emotional cycles are? Just keep track of them. For a couple of months, just write down 1–2 words that describe how you are feeling. This is not supposed to be a description of your day but rather a description of your underlying mood. For example, I could have two really horrible days, but one day I was positive and able to get through it, while the other day I was in a more defeated mood and just felt like giving up. So, really try to look at your real mood, not at all the things throughout your day that affect it. Once you have a couple months of "data collection," put them side by side and notice the patterns. Do you notice that during the middle of the month you get a little more irritable? Perhaps you seem to be the most positive at the beginning of the month. Remember, you don't need to use the same words every month, but overall, you should be able to assess whether you were generally more positive, negative, introverted, and so forth at certain times of the month.

Here are a couple of examples of actual calendars:

2013						SEPTEMBER
SUNDAY	MONDAY	TUESDAY	WEDNESDAY	THURSDAY	FRIDAY	SATURDAY
1 tired motivated goal oriented	2 upndown managed tired	3 quick to cry, anger not as in control	4 positive inspired/ visionary	5 very balanced thinking/ overwhelm	6 a little tired balanced	7 calm not even motivated but not down
8 quick to anger tired not easy to focus	9 much more tired than usual spazzed out	10 tired underlying crappy mood	11 calm, heads tired just even	12 Great I'm Am. good amount of drive + focus	13 confident positive	14 physically sick mentally balanced - low energy (not low?)
15 tired quiet introverted	16 emotionally numb	17 tired easily agitated	18 self serving	19 quiet indifferent	20 positive independent	21 introverted irritable
22 mean	23 tired wanted to try somethin not feeling well	24 calmly focused really engaged	25 hateful good low energy	26 busy body even energy	27 tired good mood	28 humble protective
29 spoken + understanding	30 emotional tired push thru it Effective					

September 2013

Sunday	Monday	Tuesday	Wednesday	Thursday	Friday	Saturday
1 happy/hyper lots of energy for the most part	2 tired / calm	3 tired / happy	4 happy / energized	5 happy / energy-ized / great mood	6 happy / tired / stressed	7 happy / hyper
8 emotional / upset / crying moody up and down	9 wild / happy / hyper	10 nappy/cranky towards end tired	11 happy / tired	12 tired / not a good night	13 okay / emotional / tired	14 happy / have energy good mood
15 positive happy/sick	16 sick / happy / too much in a lit screwed	17 sick / but super happy/silly positive	18 happy / really sick / lots of homework morning normal	19 happy good day / positive	20 positive hyper / happy	21 sick okay
22 happy/ good mood/ good energy	23 happy/ good mood/ frustrated w/ mom	24 happy/ positive/ good day	25 happy/ positive/ too much homework	26 happy/ normal	27 happy/ positive/ good day	28 happy/ really good/ lots of energy happy fun
29 very happy great day!	30 very happy/ awesome day/ positive					

Can't find the right word? Here are some words that might help you describe your moods: accepted, accomplished, aggravated, alone, amused, angry, annoyed, anxious, apathetic, ashamed, awake, bewildered, bitchy, bittersweet, blah, blank, blissful, bored, bouncy, calm, cheerful, chipper, cold, complacent, confused, content, cranky, crappy, crazy, crushed, curious, cynical, dark, depressed, determined, devious, dirty, disappointed, discontent, ditzy, dopey, dorky, drained, ecstatic, energetic, enraged, enthralled, envious, exanimate, excited, exhausted, flirty, frustrated, full, geeky, giddy, giggly, gloomy, good, grateful, groggy, grumpy, guilty, happy, high, hopeful, hot, hungry, hyper, impressed, indescribable, indifferent, infuriated, irate, irritated, jealous, jubilant, lazy, lethargic, listless, lonely, loved, mad, melancholy, mellow, mischievous, motivated, moody, nerdy, numb, okay, optimistic, peaceful, pessimistic, pissed off, pleased, recumbent, refreshed, rejected, rejuvenated, relaxed, relieved, restless, rushed, sad, satisfied, shocked, sick, silly, sleepy, smart, stressed, surprised, sympathetic, thankful, tired, touched, uncomfortable, weird, wild, wired.

Some people are able to express themselves better through colors. If that's the case, then every day, pick a color that describes your mood. You will still be able to see a pattern every month just by looking at similar colors used at the same time every month.

If you want to track your cycles and moods but writing or coloring just doesn't resonate with you, there are plenty of great apps you can download and try. New ones will always be coming out, but right now some favorites are iPeriod, WomanLog, and Period Tracker.

CHAPTER 6
Love You, Flo

It is my hope that you will learn to love Aunt Flo and treat your time with her with tenderness and a pinch of patience. Remember that her monthly visits mean your body is healthy and functioning as beautifully as it should. It's not a state of illness but rather a time of gentleness and rest. I will leave you with words from girls/women about their relationship with Flo.

"As a young teen, I dreaded the whole monthly mess, but as I matured, I realized the beauty of its function and came to appreciate the way our bodies are so specifically designed for a privileged purpose." –C.B.

"I liked the cleansing feeling, releasing feeling, and womanly feeling when I had my period. I miss it now. It made me feel young and feminine." –J.M.

"It's wonderful being a woman, and having a menstrual cycle is just part of being a beautiful woman." –C.D.

CHAPTER 7

Resources

Groups/Classes for Girls

Girls for a Change

www.girlsforachange.org

Girls for a Change (GFC) is a national organization that empowers girls to create social change. We invite young women to design, lead, fund, and implement social change projects that tackle issues girls face in their own neighborhoods.

G!rl Be Heard

www.girlbeheard.org

G!rl Be Heard uses theater as a vehicle to empower young women to become brave, confident, socially conscious leaders while exploring their own challenging circumstances.

Days for Girls:

www.daysforgirls.org

Our mission is creating a more dignified, free and

educated world through access to lasting feminine
hygiene solutions.

Hardy Girls Healthy Women
www.hghw.org
Hardy Girls Healthy Women (HGHW) is a
nonprofit organization dedicated to the health and
well-being of girls and women. Our vision is that all
girls and women experience equality, independence,
and safety in their everyday lives. To that end, our
mission is to create opportunities, develop
programs, and provide services that empower them.

Girl Talk
www.mygirltalk.org
Girl Talk is an international nonprofit peer-to-peer
mentoring program with a very simple premise:
high school girls mentor middle school girls to help
them deal with the issues they face during their
formative early teenage years. Our mission is to
help young teenage girls build self-esteem, develop
leadership skills, and recognize the value of
community service. Since 2002, our organization

has served more than 40,000 girls in forty-three states and seven countries.

Girls on the Run
www.girlsontherun.org
We inspire girls to be joyful, healthy, and confident using a fun, experience-based curriculum that creatively integrates running.

Girls Leadership Institute
www.girlsleadershipinstitute.org
The Girls Leadership Institute inspires girls to be true to themselves. We teach the practices of emotional intelligence, assertive self-expression, and healthy relationships, giving girls the skills and confidence to live as leaders.

Girls with Dreams
www.girlswithdreams.com
Founded on friends, dreams, and action, teen girls empower one another to build their best lives and take action in their own lives and the world.

I Am That Girl

www.iamthatgirl.com

A global community, a support system, and a movement of girls (8–108) turning self-doubt into self-love.

Smart-Girl

www.smart-girl.org

Founded in 1999 by four dynamic women, Smart-Girl is a Colorado-based nonprofit organization that empowers preteen and teen girls to make smart choices and become confident, capable, self-reliant young women.

One Circle Foundation

www.onecirclefoundation.org

Our programs employ evidence-based principles of a strengths-based approach and motivational interviewing strategies, and they have a strong focus on positive youth development. The age-old process of communing in a safe circle is the foundational strength of all programs.

Books about Menstruation

A Time to Celebrate: A Celebration of a Girl's First Menstrual Period by Joan Morais

Moon Time: A Guide to Celebrating Your Menstrual Cycle by Lucy H. Pearce

105 Ways to Celebrate Menstruation by Kami Mcbride

Beautiful Girl: Celebrating the Wonders of Your Body by Christiane Northrup, MD, and Kristina Tracy

Taking Charge of Your Fertility by Toni Weschler, MPH

Where to Buy Reusable Menstrual Products

Most health food stores carry unbleached cotton sanitary pads and tampons, menstrual cups, and sometimes a cloth pad or two. If you are unable to find them there, you can buy them many places online. Here is a listing of a few menstrual product companies.

Glad Rags: www.gladrags.com
Imse Vimse: www.imsevimse.us
Luna Pads: www.lunapads.com
Diva Cup: www.divacup.com
Instead: www.softcup.com
Keeper: www.keeper.com
Mooncup: www.mooncup.com
Lunette: www.lunette.com
Jade & Pearl Sponges: www.jadeandpearl.com

CHAPTER 8
Flo's Glossary

Aunt Flo: menstruation. A normal vaginal bleeding that occurs as part of a woman's monthly cycle. Every month, the body prepares for pregnancy. If no pregnancy occurs, the uterus, or womb, sheds its lining. The menstrual blood is partly blood and partly tissue from inside the uterus. It passes out of the body through the vagina.

Other names for Aunt Flo: menstruation, period, big red, little friend, on the rag, girl time, shark week, moon time, dot, time of the month, and sacred blood.

Cervix: the narrow neck-like passage forming the lower end of the uterus.

Other names for cervix: sometimes referred to as the neck of the uterus.

Fallopian Tubes: pair of tubes that carry the egg from the ovary to the uterus.

Menstruation: see *Aunt Flo*

Menstrual Cup: a flexible cup or barrier worn inside the vagina during menstruation to collect menstrual fluid. Unlike tampons and pads, the cup collects menstrual fluid rather than absorbing it. Menstrual cups are usually made from medical-grade silicone.

Ovary: the usually paired female reproductive organ that produces ova, estrogen, and progesterone.

Ovulation: the expulsion of an ovum from the ovary (usually midway in the menstrual cycle.

Sanitary Pad: an absorbent pad worn by women to absorb menstrual blood.
Other names for sanitary pad: feminine pad, sanitary napkin, and rag.

Sea Sponge: a small, natural sponge or a piece of a synthetic sponge to which a loop of string may be attached. It is inserted into the vagina to absorb the menstrual flow. Once removed, it may be washed, squeezed dry, and reused as necessary throughout menstruation.

Tampon: a plug of soft material inserted into the vagina to absorb menstrual blood.
Other names for tampon: cork, plug, and stopper.

Uterus: A hollow muscular organ located in the pelvic cavity of female mammals in which the fertilized egg implants and develops.
Other name for uterus: womb.

Vagina: The muscular canal that extends from the cervix to the outside of the body. It is usually six to seven inches in length, and its walls are lined with mucous membrane.
Other names for vagina: yoni, flower, tutu, and vag.

Made in the USA
San Bernardino, CA
04 December 2019